Keep on Taki _

The weird, wonderful and downright
wacky world of the pharmacist

To Monica,

Stephen Freeborn

With kindest regards

Steve
Freeborn .

Foreword

What does a pharmacist do?

This is a question I have been asked many times. When I hear these words, I can't help thinking of the comedian Jerry Seinfeld. In one of his shows, he asks exactly this, because as far as he can tell, all the role of a pharmacist involves is taking tablets out of a large bottle and putting them into a smaller one.

'You need a degree for that?' he asks to raucous laughter and applause from his audience.

I am a second-generation pharmacist, son of a more distinguished one: my father, Steve, who has written this book. His intention is not to show that we do far more than just put pills in bottles, but to share the experiences of a professional in the ever-changing world of healthcare in an entertaining and light-hearted way.

My dad initially had the idea to put something into words following his highly successful venture into the public-speaking arena. His talk, which shares its name with this book, is a rollercoaster ride of amusing tales from his 40 years working as a pharmacist in the NHS, and has received rave reviews. Many people who have laughed at his tales have suggested he put his words into a book for everyone to enjoy, so here we are.

My father Steve began working in the NHS at a time when potions and pills were prepared by the pharmacist in the chemist's shop, where the public would ask for a bottle of medicine for whatever ailment they had. Although he mostly worked in hospitals, he still had to make up creams and potions at a consultant's request, often out of hours and at a moment's notice. One of my earliest memories is of going into the dark old pharmacy in the hospital, watching from underneath a fume cupboard so that I wouldn't breathe anything toxic or potentially lethal into my five-year-old lungs as my dad mixed up medicines with a pestle and mortar. I'd be lying if I said that I knew there and then that pharmacy was for me, but it did look kind of fun.

So, what exactly *does* a pharmacist do? Of all the weird, wonderful and sometimes hilarious questions both my dad and I have been asked about being a pharmacist, the most notable has to be 'Does it have anything to do with farming?' We've even had people asking whether we had to go to college/university to be a pharmacist, telling us that their friend is a pharmacist because he or she has a Saturday job with Boots the Chemist.

I'm sure that they mean well.

James Freeborn

Keep on Taking the Tablets

Originally published in 2019.

This updated version produced in 2021.

Publishers - Preeta Press Ltd, Bolton, Greater
Manchester

preetapress.com

All Rights Reserved

Copyright Stephen Freeborn 2019

ISBN: 978-1-9993509-2-5

Printed by ImprintDigital.com

Front cover design – Preeta Press Ltd;

Acknowledgements

Huge thanks to the Freeborn Family – my wife Suzanne,
sons David and James and their wives Nicola and Kerstin – for their help and support.

Thanks also to everyone I have ever worked with in the NHS, and of course to the great British public. Without you all, this book could not have been written.

Alison Jack – Thank you for all of your help in editing my book.

Preeta Press – many thanks for your publishing expertise that has made this book a reality.

Contents

Introduction

When I take this tablet, how does it know where to go?

In the early days of my career, I had the pleasure of working in an Elderly Medicine Clinic. It was my job to review the patients' medications and make recommendations regarding their drugs. Having a huge interest in the world of prescription medicines, I derived plenty of satisfaction, and invaluable knowledge, from this work.

But that isn't what remains in my mind.

To this day, it's the patients themselves I remember, and their weird and wonderful questions. They were the real eye opener.

'If I have a pain in my right hand, how does the medicine know to go there?'

'My wife is taking tablets and it says on the label that they may cause drowsiness, so she shouldn't operate machinery.
Er …can she turn the washer on?'

'These instructions say I have to take the tablets with a full glass of water. Will half a glass do?'

But there's one encounter that stands out above them all.

One morning in July, there wasn't a cloud in the sky and I was feeling that all was well with the world. A charming, elegant lady came to the clinic. Well-dressed, articulate and intelligent, she sat down with me and explained her aliments and the tablets she'd been prescribed to ease them. Her explanation was clear and succinct, and I gave an inner sigh of relief. Entertaining though my more eccentric patients were, I did sometimes wonder if I'd done enough to ensure they'd actually take the medication they needed, when they needed it and in the manner in which they needed it. It made a refreshing change to be sitting across from such a sensible woman.

Or so I thought.

After we had reviewed all of the medicines that she had brought in, she asked me if I would like to see her painkillers. Music to my ears! Not only had she summed up her medical history with a level of knowledge that could have put some in the profession to shame, she'd also had the foresight to bring her medication in with her so I could see it for myself.

'That would be a great help,' I replied, waiting eagerly for her to extract blister packs of tablets and bottles of liquid from us handbag. Instead, to my amazement, the lady removed her shoe, raised her leg on to a chair and waved her foot in front of my face.

'They are there,' she said, pointing.

Between each of her toes, she had a 500mg Aspirin tablet.

'They're very strong,' she added cheerfully. 'Great for getting rid of headaches. I did a lot of walking this morning and my feet were killing me, so thought it best to put the tablets right where the pain was.'

And that was how I came to the realisation that there is far more to giving out medicines than just putting them in a bottle, which was when my priorities began to change. From being a mere supplier, I vowed to become someone who helps people really understand their medication.

Chapter 1 – How Did It All Begin?

Student days

University for me was fun, fun, fun! I was so excited to be there. Despite this being at a time when student politics was always on the news, I was too involved with the good times to participate in anything so serious.

While my more earnest peers were out marching and protesting, I was far more drawn to the excitement of planning for the university rag day procession. This was fun with a heart as the whole idea was to collect money for local charities – students giving something back to the city we'd temporarily made our home.

For the rag day parade that particularly sticks in my mind, we budding pharmacists had decided on a Charles Dickens theme for our float, representing the titles of his books with carefully painted pictures. Deaf to suggestions that a Dickens theme may have been better suited to the English department, we spent days daubing paint on to the side of our float, standing back every so often to look with pride at Miss Havisham and Magwitch, Fagin and the Artful Dodger, David Copperfield, Wackford Squeers and the Ghosts of Christmas Past, Present and Yet To Come springing to life. Well alright, the ghosts didn't exactly come to life. Let's just say the float looked fabulously literary, and we were bursting with pride at the idea of parading through the streets of the city on it when rag day finally dawned.

Rag day did finally dawn. At least, I assume the sun came up, but it was hard to tell through the gloom of the heavy rainclouds that had gathered overnight. As we donned our nineteenth-century costumes and left the Pharmacy Department on our float, the rainclouds did what rainclouds do so well.

They rained.

Unfortunately, not being artists, we weren't clued up on their materials and had used poster paint to create our Dickensian masterpiece. It was no match for a downpour that would have tested Noah's Ark, and by the time we were parading past the few hardy souls who had braved the weather to watch the procession, our wonderful artwork was nothing more than a sodden mess.

'What is that supposed to be?' asked the hardy souls, clearly unimpressed with our efforts.

My Dickensian costume, complete with a tall black hat and sombre clothing, wasn't faring too well either. Looking more like a tramp than a nineteenth-century gentleman, I cut my losses, dissociated myself from the ruined float and ran into a restaurant. Shaking my charity tin, I took a bottle of wine from a diner's table and pulled it out of the reach of his grabbing hands.

'You can have it back if you put money in my tin,' I said, my grin fading as the diner got to his feet.

He was a giant. And he was seething. Grabbing the first thing that came to hand, he let out a guttural roar and set off in pursuit as I sprinted round and round the restaurant, charity tin in one hand, ill-gotten bottle of wine in the other. Quite what he was intending to do if he caught me, armed as he was with a large baguette, I will never know. Seeing the restaurant owner lifting the phone receiver and dialling what looked suspiciously like the first of three nines, I once again decided the best course of action was to cut my losses. Dropping the bottle, I legged it through the door and ran off in the rain without a backward glance. Needless to say, I have never dined in that particular restaurant. My student days weren't all mischief and mayhem, though. I was lucky enough to see many top bands, thanks to the university students' union. The concert hall was smaller than a tennis court and had a low ceiling, but we enjoyed nights with Led Zeppelin, Slade (when they were skinheads), Curved Air, Free, Tyrannosaurus Rex and The Who (my girlfriend fell asleep during their set). Not to mention the Bonzo Dog Doo-Dah Band – who could possibly forget that night? Happy days, although it's no wonder I am a bit deaf now.

Then, of course, there were the Chemical Engineering Department's legendary cheese and wine parties. Legendarily unsophisticated, that is. In student accommodation similar in size to a shoe box, instead of fine wines and a selection of hand-made cheeses, we'd generally spend our Saturday nights with a block of cheddar and a bottle of Lambrusco, a crate of ale providing backup liquid refreshments when the wine inevitably ran out.

A social life costs money, and as students aren't exactly renowned for having healthy finances, I spent my summer vacation working in a well-known chemist's shop in the centre of a large city, wondering if this was going to be my future: study while gaining work experience, qualify, manage a shop and work my way up. The only problem was the work experience I was gaining wasn't exactly setting me up for an illustrious career as a pharmacist.

I saw very few patients or medicines in my summer job. The most exciting thing that happened was when Minnie Caldwell from *Coronation Street* came in and bought some Nine Lives Tuna for her cat. Oh, and I sold 'Good Boy' choc drops and chews for dogs, too. The stock takes on pet foods and toys were riveting: ten tall squeaky dogs with a bone, ten tall squeaky dogs without a bone...

Snore!

Even this job had its laugh-out-loud moments, though. The euphemistically named 'sports drawer' was where we kept the condoms, and I quickly learned to spot the customers sidling over to the counter, clutching an assortment of goods that they didn't really want in their hands to try to divert attention away from their whispered request for 'A pack of three, please'.

In fact, it was the size of the packs that led me to commit the biggest faux pas of my short career as a purveyor of pet accessories and condoms. The latter came in boxes of three or twelve, and most customers specified which size box they required.

Most, but not all.

As my latest customer stood at the counter, gazing around the shop with measured nonchalance as I crossed to the sports' drawer, a gardening magazine, a bottle of shampoo and a tube of children's toothpaste on the counter in front of him (the last item suggesting it was possibly too late to be asking for condoms), I arrived at the sports' drawer with no idea whether he wanted a pack of three or twelve. So, without thinking, I turned back and called across the busy shop floor.

'Would that be large or small condoms, sir?' I yelled.

My customer's eyes flew wide open and he blushed a beetroot red as shoppers all around stopped to stare. Mouth gaping open, he took a few moments to compose himself enough to answer.

'Well, I think that I'm sort of average, really,' he replied sheepishly.

9

I brought over a pack of twelve condoms. The poor bloke deserved a bit of extra fun after that experience.

On the subject of… ahem… the gentleman's anatomy, the very worst experience I had in this predominantly thankless summer job was assisting with truss measurement and fitting. I had no idea what an inguinal hernia was until I helped one of the pharmacists who was qualified in truss fitting thanks to a course supplied by the company.

Lucky man!

The three of us – customer, pharmacist and naive student – entered a small room near to the pharmacy counter. Without either hesitation or embarrassment, the customer dropped his trousers to reveal a large lump in his groin, and I couldn't help but stare at it in horror. It looked like a boiled egg was popping out of his skin.

'Please push your hernia back so that I can measure the size of truss needed,' said the pharmacist, taking the measuring tape I was handing over and asking me to write down the measurements as he shouted them out. The customer did so and the hernia popped out of

sight with an audible slurping noise. I hope that
I have not put you the reader off your dinner.

It was all a bit too much for me. The next year I
found myself a new summer job.

During the rest of my vacations, I worked in a
hospital, which was far more conducive to me
gaining the work experience I would actually
need for my career. I spent most of my time
helping to make intravenous solutions such as
saline or glucose in glass drip bottles, before the
advent of plastic. Once a solution was completed
and sterilised, it had to be checked for any
floating bits in a light box – tedious but
important work.

One day, my youthful sense of mischief got the
better of me and I decided to have some fun.
Cutting a small fish shape from a piece of paper,
I stuck it to the outside of a bottle of saline I'd
just prepared before sending it off to be checked.

When the checkers arrived, I watched while a woman called Sandra picked up my fishy bottle. This was perfect! Sandra was well known for being the most gullible member of staff, and was an easy victim for shameless pranksters like me. Grinning, I looked on as she examined the bottle, fish and all, and passed it as OK.

That was too much for me. I dissolved into helpless laughter, and Sandra fixed me with a steely glare.

'OK,' she said, 'what have you done now?'

Poor Sandra. She never did see the funny side of my pranks and chased me out of the room, threatening to brain me with the bottle.

My mischievous nature did come back to bite me in the posterior, though. I'd been asked to make a batch of nurse's hand cream, and having a healthy respect for these hard-working and dedicated people, I was determined to supply them with the best. Believing that I had followed the instructions perfectly, I filled the tubes with my quality hand cream and sent them off for distribution, daydreaming about the ways in which the female nurses may feel inclined to show their gratitude.

I didn't have to wait long before the first nurse
came to see me, but gratitude was clearly the last
thing on her mind. In fact, she was furious, and
so were her colleagues following hot on her
heels. Every single one of them had blue hands –
and the blue colouring would not come off. Far
from following the instructions to the letter, I
had put ten times the requisite amount of
dyestuff in the cream, and despite my pleas to
the contrary, no one would believe that it wasn't
yet another of my pranks.

ARRRGH!

It was my job to find every tube that had been
dispensed to each ward and bring it back, blue-
handed nurses berating me right, left and centre.

My disastrous foray into nurses' hand cream
notwithstanding, I enjoyed my time at the
hospital during my vacations from university,
and eventually left as a trusted and experienced
– if a little playful – worker.

Pre-registration year

Once I had graduated, I was required to work as
a university-qualified student pharmacist for
one year at a designated hospital in order to
become a Member of the Pharmaceutical Society.

This gave me an insight into the world that I was about to enter, as my vacation jobs had made my mind up that hospital was the place for me.

As part of my training, I observed the work going on in each area of the hospital, all of which was fascinating. But the Casualty department, now Accident and Emergency, was a particular eye opener.

On my first day, I walked into the hospital reception, wondering what the day would bring. A quick glance around the waiting room, packed to the rafters with the walking wounded, did little to steady my nerves – every ailment imaginable was represented in that one area of the hospital.

Along with one I'd never have believed had I not seen it with my own eyes.

Sitting in between an elderly lady with a bandaged wrist and a young boy trying to hold back tears as his mother gently massaged his swollen ankle, a man sat calmly gazing back at me. Embarrassed at having been caught staring, I immediately looked away and watched the steady trickle of patients coming in through the doors. But it wasn't long before my eyes were drawn back to the calm man, sitting patiently in his seat… with a blood-soaked towel round his head.

'You all right, love?' A woman's voice broke through my thoughts and I turned to offer a weak smile to the receptionist, who seemed more concerned about me than the growing queue of patients in front of her.

'Er, yes, thank you,' I managed, my attention already wandering back to the crimson towel and it's wearer. His expression was now almost serene, despite the fact that there was…

'What the devil?' I only realised I'd spoken out loud when a passing nurse touched me lightly on the arm and asked if she could do anything to help.

'No, no, I'm fine,' I stammered. 'Not so sure about…' With a vague wave in the direction of Mr Crimson Towel, I gave a shudder for good measure.

The nurse smiled kindly. 'Oh, don't worry about him,' she said. 'You'll see far more curious sights than that while you're working here.'

As the waiting room echoed to a cacophony of coughs and wheezes, I couldn't help but feel thankful she hadn't mistaken me for another patient.

'Come along now, Mr Brown.' The nurse was helping Crimson Towel to his feet and steadying him as they walked over to the treatment rooms. 'We'll have that out in no time.'

Somehow, I doubted it would be quite so simple. As the nurse and her patient walked past me, Mr Crimson Towel staggering slightly, I realised my eyes hadn't been deceived.

He really did have a claw hammer sticking out of his head.

I was one of two pre-registration pharmacy students at the hospital. Once the two of us had been introduced, we were despatched to observe a doctor on duty in Casualty.

It was a middle-aged lady with a massive cyst on her eyelid who sorted the men from the boys. As my fellow newbie and I watched, the doctor asked for a needle, sterilised the area and pierced the cyst. I have to admit, my stomach turned as yellow pus came spewing out, but before my breakfast could make a hasty reappearance, I was distracted by a 'thud' to my side. My head snapping round, nausea trumped by curiosity, I had to stifle a smile at the sight of my fellow student collapsed on the floor.

He was fine. A whiff of oxygen brought him back, but I had to wonder if he really was cut out for a career in pharmacy.

The role pharmacists offer in healthcare is often underplayed. We are approachable and available, no appointments necessary. A few years ago, before people started to have their medications delivered directly to their homes, there were over one million people visiting pharmacies daily throughout the UK to discuss health problems. These numbers may have reduced, but the potential of the pharmacist to pass on good advice for a healthy life is incredible.

I remember being out with friends one evening and the conversation turned to healthcare. One of my friends, an educated lady, told the assembled company that although she gets a prescription every month from the doctor for Aspirin, but never takes it.

'Why ever not?' I asked.

'Because I don't want to take Aspirin,' she replied. 'It doesn't agree with me.'

'So why do you keep getting the prescriptions?'

My friend looked at me incredulously. 'I don't want to let the doctor down, of course!' she replied as if it was the most obvious thing in the world.

And there you have it. People are often more honest about their conditions with their pharmacist than they'd ever be in the GP's surgery. Even those who've never sat in a doctor's chair can be convinced by a pharmacist to consider doing something about their smoking habit or their flaky scalp.

The pharmacist has a caring and important role in society, and I'm proud to be part of a profession that will continue to offer a personal

and invaluable service to the health and
wellbeing of the public for years to come.

Chapter 2 – Early Days As A Qualified Pharmacist

I got my first job as a fully qualified member of the Royal Pharmaceutical Society at a large teaching hospital, hoping that it would provide more stimulation than my university vacation jobs and pre-registration year.

I was to be disappointed. It was more of the same old stuff. In fact, in some ways it was worse. As the dispensary in the main hospital was one floor above the reception, the prescriptions came up in a lift, were prepared by us newbie pharmacists and sent back down. For the first few weeks of my career as a fully fledged pharmacist, I didn't see one single patient.

Visiting the powers that be to moan about my sorry lot in life, I think I must have worn them into submission. Afterwards, I was moved to the eye unit and finally experienced the joy of dispensing medication directly to the people who needed it.

I was now working in a small, old-fashioned dispensary with oak drawers and shelves. It was a cosy, friendly environment, and I was happy to find that my colleagues shared my mischievous sense of humour. We enjoyed many a belly laugh, as we went about the serious business of providing our patients with the solutions they needed.

However, as I was soon to learn, a mischievous sense of humour can be overdone.

I was working with a pharmacy technician with whom I'd become pretty friendly, dispensing a prescription for Chloramphenicol eye drops. My job was to check the preparation, which I duly did, then handed it back to the pharmacy technician.

He poked his head out of the pharmacy's serving window and called the patient over.

'Mr Nelson, your eye drops are ready.'

Looking over his shoulder at me, he added, 'If he's wearing an eye patch, it'll be hilarious.' Warming to his theme, he trilled, 'Kiss me, Hardy,' and fell about with laughter.

Trying to point towards the serving window without being too obvious about it, I muttered, 'Um, I wouldn't…'

'It's just a bit of 'armless fun,' my colleague interrupted me. 'Get it? Armless?'

'Please stop,' I said, desperately flicking my eyes towards the window.

'I see no ships!' shrieked the hysterical technician.

'It's not bloody funny, you know!' roared a voice from behind him. Mr Nelson had been standing at the window ever since he'd heard his name, and was clearly as furious as my hapless colleague was amused. Baring his teeth, Mr Nelson snatched his eye drops from the technician's hand as the latter tried, unsuccessfully, to control himself. With a snort of laughter, my colleague delivered his parting shot.

'I wish you *victory* in your recovery. You're not called Horatio, by any chance…?'

With a growl that sounded suspiciously like 'I will be reporting you', Mr Nelson, who may or may not have been called Horatio, stormed away. I advised my technician colleague that his teasing had probably been a tad inappropriate, to which the cheeky so-and-so replied:

'You could have told me he was behind me.'

That particular technician didn't work with me in the eye unit again. And Horatio? I believe he decided to bite the bullet and pay out for private healthcare.

As coincidence would have it, not long afterwards, I experienced life as a patient in the eye unit myself. Settling down to watch *Match of the Day*, I decided to treat myself to a glass of Pomagne (the Prosecco of the day). I removed the foil wrapping and protective wire cage, and was readying myself to pop the plastic cork when…

   'BANG!'

The plastic cork shot into my eye without any prompting from me whatsoever.

I ran to the bathroom mirror to inspect the damage. To my horror, the white of the eye had turned completely red and I collapsed on the floor, shaking violently. Then everything went black.

The next thing I recall, I was waking up in a bed in a dimly lit room, the gentle sounds of grunting and farting all around me. I studied my surroundings with my good eye and took in rows of patients lying on beds.

Grunting? Farting? Beds? I could only be in one place – a hospital ward!

For three weeks I had to stay in the hospital bed, moving as little as possible, much to the delight of my colleagues. The prankster had turned into the victim as I became the butt of every hospital-related wind-up known to the medical profession, from the amorous 'nurse' who was actually my bearded colleague in fancy dress to my least favourite food appearing on the menu for seven days in a row, to the joke-shop 'floater' left in my bed pan.

Needless to say, I wasn't quite so quick to try for a laugh at my colleagues' expense after those three weeks of torture.

Talking of floaters, my sight did gradually come back in my injured eye, but it has never truly recovered. I have many floaters to this day – but not the sort found in bed pans.

The power of the placebo

Back at work, I spent some time in charge of the Maternity and Gynaecology unit pharmacy, and this was when I learnt the power of suggestion.

A prescription was presented at the pharmacy for some aqueous cream, a mild preparation often used to rehydrate dried skin. As I invited the patient to take a seat while she waited, the pharmacy phone rang.

'When you label the aqueous cream,' said the consultant who had sent the patient over, 'would you simply call it "The Cream"?' He went on to ask me to tell the patient that it was a very special preparation, guaranteed to succeed where all others had failed.

'We've tried everything,' the consultant explained to me, 'but still the patient complains of a persistent pain in her left buttock. Tell her if she wants any more of "The Cream", she can come back and see me.'

A month later, the patient came back for some more of 'The Cream'. As I dispensed the humble aqueous solution into its special packaging, she said it was the best treatment she'd ever experienced and all the pain had gone for the first time in months.

Since then, I have never underestimated the power of the placebo.

Doctor Death

In 1976, I was lucky enough to be accepted on a University Clinical Pharmacy Master's course after a tricky interview. I was to receive full pay for one year while I studied.

Absolutely brilliant! I loved every minute of it, doing ward rounds with consultants, sitting in lectures with trainee medics and conducting research into the use of Pethidine, a drug to give pain relief in childbirth. From this research, I was able to publish some very useful and relevant findings that are still quoted today.

It was sometimes a bit scary, though.

'Now then, Mr Pharmacist, this elderly patient is extremely unwell,' the consultant turned to me and said on one of my ward rounds. 'He has been treated for a severe chest infection with an antibiotic as recommended by Bacteriology, but he is not improving. In fact, he is getting worse. Should we change antibiotic?'

Should we *what*? Why are you asking me? You're the consultant!

'Um, perhaps it would be better to change the antibiotic rather than increase the dose of the current one.' I remember feeling rather pleased with this response, which was in accordance with my newfound learnings from my Clinical Pharmacy course. Unfortunately, the next day the very ill patient died, and from then on, the medical registrars gave me the nickname Dr Death.

Yes, hilarious!

Acupuncture?

During my research study into Pethidine, I worked in the maternity delivery suite of a well-known hospital in the northwest of England. Every day I walked in to the sound of screaming from the delivery suite, which wasn't unusual, but on one occasion it was particularly loud.

'Just bloody give it to me!' bellowed the voice of a mother-to-be. At least, I assumed it was the mother-to-be. 'Give it to me! Give it to me!'

It was no good, curiosity had got the better of me. Give what to whom? I had to find out. There was quite a group of nurses gathered outside the delivery suite, offering words of encouragement to the staff within.

'Give her what she wants.'

'No! She was adamant she didn't want it when she came in.'

'That's right, she said her husband had convinced her acupuncture would work.'

27

'Piffle, that was then. I think she's changed her mind…'

'AAAARGH!' roared the mother-very-soon-to-be. 'Just… puff-puff… give it… puff-puff… to me… puff…'

'No!' bellowed a man's voice. 'She doesn't need it. It's all in her mind. Acupuncture, that's the answer.'

'Acupuncture?' I wouldn't have believed it possible, but the almost-a-mother-another-few-pushes-should-do-it managed to raise her voice even further. 'Acu-flipping-puncture? Get that bastard away from me or I will stab him with his bloody pins when I get out of here. I'm in agony. Give me that gas and air, NOW!'

Chapter 3 – Moving Up The Ladder

Flying low

After I'd finished the Master's, I followed my ambition to move up the career ladder by applying for staff pharmacist jobs in local hospitals. It wasn't long before I was invited for interview, and brimming with confidence, I prepared carefully for the big day.

On the morning of my first interview, I rose early after a good night's sleep, feeling alert and positive. Dressing in a smart suit and crisp white shirt, I armed myself with my meticulous notes and carefully crafted questions, all designed to show that I had put a lot of work into researching this particular position and this particular hospital. Arriving at reception, I smiled brightly at the woman behind the desk and announced my name and reason for being there.

'Oh yes,' she replied, returning my smile, 'you want the second floor. Take the corridor to the right of the lifts, and you'll see the pharmacy you need signposted. Good luck!'

'Thanks,' I said with another smile, confident that I wouldn't need luck. This baby was in the bag.

On arrival at the pharmacy, I again announced my arrival and was invited to take a seat and help myself to coffee from the nearby machine. Avoiding the coffee machine like the plague – there was no way I was going to jeopardise my chances with a mistimed coffee spillage – I settled myself on a seat, nodded a hello to the other candidates and waited to be called in. Nothing was going to stop me now. The interview was a disaster. As I strode into the interview room, notes in hand, all my hours of careful preparation amounted to nothing as the zip on my trousers simply crumbled. It was awful. I couldn't concentrate on what was being said, only on my flies that were now gaping open, revealing the colour of my underpants to the grim-faced interview panel in front of me.

The moment I heard, 'Do you have any questions for us?' I mumbled a hasty no, already shuffling towards the door. In the corridor, I removed my jacket and draped it over my arms, strategically covering my embarrassment. My carefully crafted notes and questions went in the rubbish bin just outside the hospital's main entrance. My trousers were hurled with even less ceremony into the rubbish bin as soon as I'd reached the sanctuary of my home and changed my clothes.

Suffice it to say, I didn't get the job.

The crazy world of the hospital pharmacist

The proud owner of a new suit with an extra strong zip on the trousers, I soon rediscovered my confidence and rebuilt my interview techniques, and before long I'd landed a job as a staff pharmacist at a paediatric hospital. It was wonderful. I was able to take my newly acquired clinical training out into the real world with the introduction of clinical pharmacy ward rounds.

I have tremendous admiration for my colleagues in the NHS. This great institution, I believe, marks out the UK as a wonderfully civilised place to live – we all pay for healthcare not only for ourselves, but for everyone else in the country. It must have been terrible pre-NHS, when families had to decide whether to spend their money on food for the table or a visit to the doctor when someone was ill.

In my young days, pharmacy had to provide a service twenty-four hours a day, seven days a week, including unpaid on-call work which was sometimes a bit tricky and emotional. One of my call outs to the paediatric hospital was at 2 am, when I was required to supply an injection for a child with leukaemia. I prepared the injection under the proper sterile conditions and took it to the ward for the nursing staff to administer.

It was a sad sight. A nurse sat at the bedside of a small child. The large haematoma on his bottom lip kept leaking blood and the nurse was continuously mopping it up. She looked absolutely exhausted, but all her care and attention was focused on making the night as comfortable as possible for that desperately sick child.

As I handed over the injection, I commented that I bet she would be relieved when her shift was over. She told me that her shift had actually finished six hours earlier, but nothing was going to drag her away from that child in his time of need.

This is what the NHS is all about. This is why I hate to hear anyone criticise it.

Another call out at a more civilised time – 10 pm, to be precise – saw me looking for a drug called Naloxone, which is used to reverse opioid poisoning. Finding what I needed, I took the Naloxone to the Intensive Care Unit (ICU), expecting to see the doctor who had requested it tending to some poor addict who'd gone too far in search of – well, whatever it is addicts search for. Utopia? A high? A hit? Just to feel normal? It's a sad life, however you look at it.

To my amazement, when I arrived in the ICU, the doctor wasn't standing beside a shivering addict; he was at the side of a small child, who was completely sparked out.

'What on earth happened?' I whispered, handing over the Naloxone to the clearly concerned medic.

He rolled his eyes. 'Apparently,' he said, 'the child got hold of his father's "medicine" and took some.'

'His *medicine*? But Naloxone is to counteract…'

'I know,' replied the doctor, giving me a meaningful stare.

The poor child was struggling to breathe, but his recovery was one of the most remarkable things that I have ever seen. The moment the doctor had injected the Naloxone into him, his eyes fluttered open and he asked for his mum. The doctor and I exchanged huge smiles of relief and I made my way back to the pharmacy, happy that all had ended well.

That relief, as it turned out, was somewhat premature. As I was closing up the pharmacy, content that all seemed quiet and I could return home to my bed, a nurse raced out of the ICU.

'Quick!' she said urgently. 'We need more Naloxone.'

The child was in trouble again. Unfortunately, Naloxone only takes effect for a short time and he had relapsed, so the doctor needed to administer more antidote until the longer acting opioid had worn off.

Sometimes I wonder at the suitability of certain parents to be in charge of a small child. And sometimes I can understand the logic of the parents, but it doesn't always make it right.

A lady came to the pharmacy with her child and complained that the liquid antibiotic that she had received for his earache didn't seem to be doing much good. In fact, all it was doing was making him miserable, and the liquid was messing up his clothes. The child himself cast a doleful look in my direction and scratched his ear. Then he scratched it again, and kept on scratching it.

'Hmm, that's clearly not right,' I said. 'May I see the medication?'

The bottle that the mother produced from her back and handed to me had a dropper in the top. The instructions were that she was to administer 1ml orally.

'You've been following the correct dosage?' I asked, looking up from the bottle to meet her concerned gaze.

'To the letter,' she replied. Well, as it turned out, this wasn't strictly true.

'You've been giving him 1ml?'

'Yes.'

'Orally?'

The mother sighed, clearly exasperated by the questioning. 'Yes, I've been putting it in his ear.'

'You've been *what*?'

'Aurally,' she replied, impatiently. 'I was told to give it aurally…'

Occasionally new drugs become available that are classed as 'un-licenced', and it is up to the consultant in charge to make the decision as to whether or not the drug can be used. Which puts me in mind of another very poorly child.

This particular child was critically ill on the leukaemia ward. Her parents were at her bedside, the mood was sombre and the medical staff were facing the heart-breaking prospect of seeing yet another youngster who should have their whole life ahead of them slowly slipping away. However, there was a chance – just a tiny chance – she might survive if we used an un-licenced drug. There was plenty of good supporting evidence that this drug was a huge breakthrough, so the consultant in charge asked if it was possible for me to obtain it with his approval.

There was just one problem. The un-licenced drug was only available from a pharmaceutical company in Italy at that time. And I didn't speak a word of Italian. Needless to say, my initial conversation with the company got us precisely nowhere.

Then I had an idea. Telling my colleagues, I wouldn't be long, I headed for the exit.

'Wait!' called the consultant. 'Er, we need you here, kind of urgently. Where the heck are you going?'

'Oh,' I replied, 'you know the garage along the road? The one with the tasty looking Ferrari in the window?'

'I do,' said the consultant, the gleam in her eye suggesting she had drooled over this particular motor as much as I had. 'But it's not really the time to go car shopping.'

'Trust me, I'm a pharmacist,' I replied with a grin. I could have sworn the words 'That's what worries me' followed me out of the door.

I promise I didn't even give the shining Ferrari a second glance as I bundled into the garage and waylaid a passing mechanic.

'You specialise in Italian cars, is that right?' I asked.

'Yes,' he replied, looking at me suspiciously.

'So, do any of you guys actually speak Italian?'

My idea wasn't as madcap as it may sound. To my immense relief, there were two Italian speakers at the garage, and once I'd explained to the garage manager why I needed to borrow one of them for a while to translate on a telephone call, he was only too happy to help.

Back at the hospital, I wrote a short script detailing the situation, the name of the consultant and the drug we required, handed it to the mechanic Roberto and rang the pharmaceutical company again. After a great deal of rapid Italian, the mechanic turned to me and asked how much of the drug we needed, then passed on my reply to the company rep on the other end of the line in Italy.

With a friendly 'Ciao', the mechanic finally rang off. He turned to me and said that the drug would be delivered in a few days and to call him back if it didn't appear, then headed for the exit to return to work, my heartfelt thanks following him to the door.

I'm delighted to say, this story has a happy ending. The drug arrived four days later, the consultant immediately set about treating the patient, and the results were better than any of us had dared to hope. The child improved rapidly and was eventually able to be discharged and return home. The report we sent back to the pharmaceutical company, to add to the evidence that the drug was effective, was extremely positive, but even more wonderful was seeing the young patient's beaming face as she and her eternally grateful parents turned to say goodbye to us. Everyone involved in her recovery had gathered to wave her off – doctors, nurses, pharmacists, even the Italian speaking mechanic and his boss had dropped in – and there wasn't a dry eye in the place.

Growing up

It was while I was working at the children's hospital that my wife gave birth to a lovely, healthy baby boy. I was delighted to become a father, but with it came the realisation of just what turmoil the parents of the young patients went through. There's little more tragic than the untimely death of a child, and now I was a father myself, the tragedies I was seeing on a daily basis really started to get to me. I kept relating the problems to my own child.

For my own sanity, and to introduce my clinical ideas to a wider audience, I decided to move into adult medicine and surgery. Especially adult surgery. So, my next step was to become the pharmacist in charge at a local general hospital. This suited me perfectly as it meant I still had plenty of time to spend with the family.

The dispensary was a busy one, and with an increased workload comes an increased chance of an encounter with an eccentric patient. Like the gentleman who came over to collect his completed prescription for an anti-diarrhoeal preparation.

'Have you taken these before?' I asked, handing the package of tablets over. The patient shook his head, so I tapped my finger on the instruction label and read, 'One to be taken with each loose stool.'

He looked at the instruction label, a perplexed frown creasing his forehead.

'Eh?' he said.

'Take one tablet,' I repeated, 'with each loose stool.'

'What if I'm not near one?'

'What, a toilet?'

'No,' he said, lifting the waiting room chair he'd been sitting on and thrusting it towards me, 'a loose stool.'

A gentle word in his ear put him right.

Continuing the stool-related theme (the seating kind, not the faecal kind), I would always invite patients to, 'Take a seat please,' if they arrived before I'd finished preparing their prescription or when I was serving someone else.

'Certainly,' replied one wag, picking up a chair and turning towards the door, 'where would you like me to take it to?'

The devil's in the detail

There were occasions when junior doctors would clash with equally inexperienced pharmacists. The pharmacists would sometimes view the doctors as a little pedantic, their requests as over detailed. But the oversight of a small detail can lead to big trouble, and did in the case of one unfortunate woman.

A prescription arrived in the pharmacy for atropine eye drops to be put into the patient's right eye twice daily. Atropine, otherwise known as belladonna, comes from the deadly nightshade plant and works by relaxing the iris and immobilising the muscles around the eye, causing the pupil to dilate. Centuries ago, it was used in Italy by women wanting to enlarge their pupils to appear more beautiful – hence the name *belladonna* (Italian for beautiful woman) – but it fell out of favour because it made the vision blurred, and in some cases caused near blindness.

Under strict medical conditions, though, the drops could be highly effective in treating eye ailments – as long as the instructions were correct. Unfortunately for the lady we were treating, her right eye was actually her *good* eye. It was her left eye that needed treatment. Within days of starting to put the drops into her good right eye, as per the instructions on the packet, the poor woman was virtually blind in both eyes. We had to keep her in hospital until the drops wore off, social services were called in to look after her children, and despite the fact her right eye did eventually make a full recovery.

Since that incident, I have always insisted that doctors write as much detail as possible of the treatment required clearly on the prescription and then talk to the patient to ensure that they agree with the instructions, no matter how pedantic that may make me in the eyes of the younger and less experienced pharmacists. The consequences of a prescribing error can be too horrific to bear.

Pharmacist on call

My stints on call while working in my local hospital threw up a number of unusual incidents, not least the night I was called into Casualty to see a newly arrived patient.

It wasn't hard to find the latest emergency. In a cubicle, surrounded on all sides by curtains, a man was screaming fit to raise the dead.

'Help me! Please, help me!' At first glance, I thought that the patient was a black man, but on closer examination, I discovered he was actually a white man covered in a layer of tar. Oh, and feathers. Who could forget the feathers?

I was asked to make something to remove the tar with as little pain to the patient as possible. Rushing off to the pharmacy, I put together an oil-based concoction as quickly as I could, then returned to Casualty. The mixture worked well and the tar began to come off.

It was then we realised why he'd been screaming so loudly. The tar had been covering fresh cuts all over his body. He must have been in agony!

As he calmed down, he began to relate his tale. It turned out he was actually a career burglar who had chosen the wrong house to break into. Unfortunately for him, he had targeted the home of a notorious hard man whose crimes amounted to a lot more than housebreaking. The hapless burglar had been caught red handed by the hard man and his cronies, roughed up at knifepoint, taken out on to farmland, and rolled in tar and creosote in the chicken coup. I never thought I'd feel sorry for a housebreaker, but seeing this poor man, quite literally tarred and feathered, I couldn't help but feel a little sympathetic. The punishment seemed to outweigh the crime quite drastically.

At least the hard man and his hired muscle had the decency to drop the burglar off at the local hospital once they'd finished with him. One has to be thankful for small mercies, I suppose, and hope that the career burglar left his life of crime behind after that experience.

Another memorable on-call incident occurred when I was driving up the long driveway to the hospital. Walking along the middle of the road, coming towards me, was a shadowy figure. As I came closer, I slowed down to avoid the figure, and it was then I noticed that it was a woman – who was completely naked.

I stopped the car and opened the window.

'Excuse me, would you like a lift?' I shouted to her

The woman turned tail and darted back towards the hospital, disappearing near to the psychiatric block. I followed on slowly, parking up near the main hospital and going into the porters' office.

'I hate to disturb you,' I said, 'but there's a naked woman running around outside the psychiatric block…'

I've never seen porters move so fast. They raced out of the office and I joined them, my marathon training coming in handy that night.

We eventually found the naked woman cowering in the bushes in the hospital grounds. As one of the porters put his jacket round her to keep her warm and protect her modesty, she did her best to explain her strange behaviour.

'I have got snakes in my head,' she assured us. Then, seeing that wasn't convincing us much, she proclaimed, 'I can make the wind blow!'

As soon as we'd returned her safely to her ward, the porters and I made our way back over to the main body of the hospital, shivering in the cold of the night as the adrenaline rush receded.

'Sorry to have brought you out in the middle of winter,' I said to the porter whose jacket was still wrapped around the psychiatric patient.

'Not at all,' he replied with a grin. 'That's the most exciting thing that's occurred in months!'

Chapter 4 – Chief Pharmacist

Out of the blue, an opportunity arose for me to apply for the position of chief pharmacist at a large general hospital, the pharmacy staff numbering almost a hundred. I was very young at the time and didn't expect to even get an interview, so I couldn't believe my luck when I got the job. What a great opportunity to spread my ideas and clinical training.

The staff at all levels throughout the hospital were supportive of me right from the start and everything was going well until I first visited the pharmacy store, which contained all of the hospital's medication. What a shock I had then. The store was situated in the basement of the larger of two main hospitals and all the staff were walking about in wellies. I couldn't believe what I was seeing – the store was a foot deep in water. It had been raining hard for days, but this was ridiculous.

I asked the pharmacy storeman how long the situation had been going on.

'Oh, for years. There is no money to improve things, so all the hospital management can offer us is sympathy.'

I called the hospital photographer who took pictures of us standing in the water in our wellies, looking glum. Then armed with these photos, I hijacked the Area Health Authority meeting, which was being held in the hospital boardroom.

'Until I receive some assurance that you'll do something to rectify this situation,' I said, 'I will not leave this room.'

After much humming and hawing and suspicious looks in my direction, the authorities persuaded me to leave them in peace with promises that they would look into it. Feeling a little deflated, I allowed myself to be escorted to the door, which was shut very firmly the moment I was through it. Actually, if I'm honest, they didn't even wait until I was all the way through.

'Right,' I muttered as the closing door shunted me out into the corridor, 'I'll believe that when I see it.'

But believe it I did. Two days later, I received a note to say that the Area Health Authority had decided to release £15,000 to upgrade the drains outside the pharmacy stores.

Ask and ye shall receive. Result!

Doing the rounds

Chief pharmacists at the time mainly did admin work and rarely left the office, but my style was to be out and about. I used to visit the smaller hospitals under the responsibility of the large general hospital, one of which had a ward dedicated to the treatment of Tuberculosis (TB), others specialising in paediatric care.

I was on the TB ward one cold day in December, looking over the patients' prescriptions that were detailed on charts at the end of the beds, then glancing at the patients themselves. Most were asleep and all appeared calm – until I reached the last bed on the ward.

Here, the patient was awake, bright red and sweating profusely. What a shame! He was clearly very ill.

As I went closer, my leg touched the side of the bed. It rippled and wobbled, and I jumped back in alarm and scooted off to the sister's office.

'There's a what?' she asked, looking askance at my garbled account. Taking a deep breath, I tried again, this time speaking as slowly and clearly as I could manage with my mind whirling, looking for a reasonable explanation as to why a hospital bed would be rippling.

'The man at the end of the ward,' I gasped. 'His bed is wobbling. And it's red hot.'

The sister laughed. 'It's wobbling because it's a water bed,' she said. Ah, that explained a lot. 'But I don't like the sound of the "red hot" bit.'

Striding down the ward, a concerned pharmacist hot on her heels, the sister approached the patient in the water bed and checked the controls.

'Well really,' she said, turning the temperature dial down, 'when I said keep him warm, I didn't mean poach him like a breakfast egg!'

I thoroughly enjoyed joining the consultants for their ward rounds, which proved to be both entertaining and educational. Each consultant, man or woman, was a strong character who didn't suffer fools, but they all had their little foibles. One was a keen follower of horse racing, and every time a race meeting was going on, his rounds would take in regular trips to the recreation room. No matter what the patients in there were watching on the television, they soon had to become accustomed to the picture regularly changing to show a stretch of green and a group of highly-strung racehorses chomping at their bits and nipping at each other's flanks.

And then they'd be off, thundering over the downs of Goodwood or the jumps of Aintree, an intelligent and well-respected man screaming his horse on to victory or otherwise (usually otherwise) as patients, pharmacists and nurses looked on. Then with a 'Bugger it, I knew I should have backed the favourite' and the occasional 'Woohoo, I'm in the money!' he'd come back to the reality of hospital rounds and off we'd go on to the wards again.

Another consultant always asked the same question of any new medic on his ward round:

'What is the normal Phenytoin blood level in a patient?'

Eager to show their knowledge, the junior doctors would invariably reply, '10–20 mcg per ml.'

'That is incorrect,' the consultant would say with a chuckle. 'It is zero if the patient isn't on Phenytoin.'

The juniors fell for it every time!

One rather rotund male consultant told me a story about the full-length mirror in his bedroom.

'I hate the wretched thing,' he said with feeling. 'I can't avoid it – it's right next to the door.'

Deciding he'd found a sympathetic ear as I nodded, he went on to explain how his wife had caught him examining his belly in the mirror one evening.

'I think I must be anorexic,' he'd said to her. 'Every time I look into this mirror, I see a big fat man.'

'No, you're not anorexic, dear,' she'd replied. 'You are a big fat man.'

I remember entering one particular ward in the hospital to join a ward round only to be greeted by a terrible smell coming from the kitchen. I bobbed my head in to see a junior nurse stirring a pan on the hob.

'What are you doing?' I asked politely.

'I was asked to warm some blood before we put it into a patient,' she replied, looking up from the bubbling red liquid to give me a sunny smile. I felt almost mean advising her that the blood should actually have remained in its bag and been gently warmed to room temperature.

Doing the rounds another day, I entered the ward to find the curtains were drawn all round a bed. This in itself wasn't unusual; what was unusual was the woman's head peering out over the top of the curtains. A young nurse, having been given the strictest instructions that the patient must remain bedridden, had heaved a commode up on to the bed when the poor woman wanted to relieve herself.

I left it to the ward sister to put that nurse right.

Where am I supposed to put them?

At the large general hospital, the pharmacy window was situated at the end of a long hall. On dispensary duty one day, I was baffled by the strange antics of a patient who kept walking past the window, back and forth.

Eventually he stopped and pressed the bell for attention.

As I opened the window and he thrust his head in, I looked at him in amazement. There was a suppository sticking out of each nostril, melting and dripping down to his top lip.

'I was breathing much better before I was told to use these,' he said.

It transpired he had been prescribed aminophylline suppositories for his asthma. These work very well – if they're used in the correct manner.

Inviting the patient to come with me into a quiet side room, I explained where he was supposed to have inserted the suppositories. As I spoke, his expression became more and more shocked, and when I got out a patient leaflet to add credence to my words, he could contain himself no longer.

'That's disgusting, is that!'

Well let's face it, having suppositories dripping from the nostrils isn't a great look.

This incident did get me thinking about how the instructions on medication labels can confuse even the brightest of people. One particular patient springs immediately to mind: an academic, well respected in his field and well-known in the area for his studies and lectures. But as I dispensed his medication and asked if he was clear on what to do with it, an unhappy expression crossed his face. He sat down, clutching the pack in his hands, read the label a couple of times over, and then stared at me in despair.

'I'm confused,' he said. 'I don't know what to do.'

I asked him what the problem was.

'How can I get home?'

'How did you get here?'

'On the bus.'

'Well go home the same way. There's a regular service from right outside the…'

'But there might be children on the bus.'

'Sorry, I don't understand.'

'It says on this bottle *keep out of the reach of children.*'

Scary experience

In the 1980s, the treatment of cancer was developing rapidly and we had the opportunity to use newly developed injections. But they had to be prepared under very strict aseptic conditions. I made a bid to hospital management to buy a special cabinet for the pharmacy so we could prepare the injections, and to my delight I was successful.

Everything was going well, until the day when a consultant rang and asked if we could prepare a newly released drug to treat acute myeloid leukaemia. I, of course, said yes, I would be happy to provide her with the help she needed, using our new equipment.

The medication arrived. It consisted of two solutions that needed to be mixed together. Simple. I put on my safety gown, gloves and goggles, swabbed down the cabinet and set to work. All was going well until I mixed the two medications together. At this point, the plastic syringe suddenly started to lose its shape. Staring at the offending object, I could only watch in horror as it melted before my eyes.

With red fumes pouring out of the cabinet, I let out a small scream and dropped everything, running out of the room and stripping off my clothes as I went. The technical staff must have thought I had gone mad! I ran to the shower in the gents across the corridor, gave myself a good wash, and then went home for a change of clothes.

I learned a valuable lesson that day – always read the label. Which in this case clearly said, 'Only use glass apparatus for reconstitution.'

Hammy experience

Even though my main job was a hospital pharmacist I sometimes did locum work in community pharmacy shops at the weekends to help to feed and clothe my growing family. This was exactly what I was doing, in a pharmacy next door to a veterinary surgery, when a woman came in holding a hamster.

The poor creature was looking a little the worse for wear. In fact, it had patches of fur missing and was covered in red spots, but being a pharmacist, I couldn't do a great deal for it.

That wasn't going to put the pet owner off, though.

'Well, what's wrong with him?' she demanded.

'Sorry, I'm not very good with hamsters,' I replied.

'Hmmph, call yourself a vet?'

At this point, she dropped the poor hamster on to the counter and stormed out, leaving me to take the creature next door to get it the care it needed.

Chapter 5 – How Do I Use It?

After ten years of working across two sites in two different dispensaries, we pharmacists were finally rewarded. The powers that be decided to extend the larger hospital into one new all singing-and-dancing version and close the smaller of the two hospitals, and we were to get a brand new pharmacy. Wow, it was terrific seeing the new department being built with state-of-the-art facilities, a large dispensary with a decent waiting area for outpatients and all the mod cons.

We soon settled into our new premises and got back to doing what we did best: taking care of patients and the labelling of medicines. It wasn't long, though, before we realised that our dispensary may have changed, but the patients themselves remained as weird and wonderful as ever.

Walking down the hospital corridor, a spring in my step as I was still euphoric about the new pharmacy, I noticed a patient struggling along ahead of me. Each step was causing her to yelp in pain. The poor thing! Climbing off my cloud without hesitation, I caught up with her and asked her if I could help.

She told me that she was making her way to Accident and Emergency. 'I have a problem "down below",' she whispered, going on to tell me that she'd been prescribed some pessaries to cure her problem. 'But they're just making things much worse.'

'I'm a pharmacist,' I replied brightly. 'Would you mind if I took a look at the pessaries?'

She handed me the box and I checked the expiry date. They were well within date, so what else could be wrong with them? Perhaps they came from a rogue batch – I'd need to know so I could get all the packs recalled.

Removing a pessary from the box, I unwrapped the silver foil from around it so I could have a good look at it.

'Oh!' she said. 'Are you supposed to take the foil off?'

To inhale or not to inhale

Of all the medications I have dispensed, inhalers have probably caused more misunderstandings than any other. Backed up by evidence that some patients have real difficulties using this particular medication, I decided to carry out research that involved asking 100 patients to show me how they used them when I dispensed their inhalers.

It proved to be an eye opener.

'Here you are, sir, this is a Salbutamol inhaler,' I said, handing the small plastic contraption to the patient in front of me. 'You need to take one or two puffs up to four times daily. Have you used one of these before?'

'Yes, it's rubbish.'

'Oh! Would you mind showing me how you use it?'

The man shook the inhaler, which is good technique. He then took off the protective cover from the mouthpiece – again, best practice. I've been amazed by how many people don't do that. That, however, was where his technique and best practice parted ways.

Putting his hand in his trouser pocket, he rummaged around for a while and pulled out a metal dessert spoon.

He then squirted a dose from the inhaler on to the spoon, put it into his mouth and swallowed.

Another inhaler user arrived at the pharmacy window and I went through the same routine. I asked if the inhaler had been of any benefit, and again the patient said no.

'Would you mind showing me how you use the inhaler, please?'

'No problem.' The patient unbuttoned his shirt and squirted his inhaler on to his chest, rubbing at the spot for a while before buttoning up his shirt again.

'Ah,' I said. 'Has anyone told you to put the inhaler in your mouth and breath in as you push the top of the canister?'

'Why would I put it in my mouth? It's for my chest.'

Another day, another inhaler user.

Surely this bright young woman will know how to use it properly, I thought hopefully.

Wrong!

When I asked her to show me how she used her inhaler, she shook it (so far, so good), removed the protective cap (yes, yes!), and then… aimed the inhaler away from herself.

Noooo!

Squirting a dose into the air, she took a deep breath and hoped for the best.

I told her that she was supposed to put the inhaler into her mouth. She told me not to be ridiculous. The doctor had told her what to do.

'He said, "Press the top of the inhaler and breathe in,"' she said triumphantly. 'He said nothing about putting it in my mouth.'

A patient with an allergy to dog hairs came to me, brandishing the inevitable inhalers and declaring them to be 'Useless'.

'I have three dogs,' she said, 'and this thing isn't doing anything to relieve my allergy.'

I took the inhalers from her and examined them. From what she'd told me, they really should be doing the trick.

Handing the inhalers back, I asked her how she was using them.

'I'm telling you, these inhalers do not help. I have been spraying the dogs four times daily and I am no better.'

Internal or external

On any hospital ward, you will find a clinic room, and each room will contain two stock medicine cupboards. One is for internal medicines and one for external medicines. It's quite self-explanatory – the internal medicines are the ones we swallow and the external are those we use on the outside of our bodies.

There's a very good reason why the two are kept separate. Imagine that I have a bottle of linctus that I have been taking for a tickly cough. No matter how careful I have been, there is usually an odd drip of syrup seeping from under the cap when I reseal the bottle. Imagine that I also have been using some haemorrhoid cream. The end of the tube, which I throw into my medicine chest after use, hits the linctus bottle.

Can you see where I am going with this?

My next door neighbour Jean then develops a tickly cough and, knowing I'm a pharmacist, pops in to see me.

'Hello, Jean,' I say. 'I have some simple linctus that should help. Here we are, have a good swig.'

I then don't see Jean for days. She has forgotten her cough – she *daren't* cough, because the bacteria from my linctus bottle have given her gastroenteritis.

Of course, I would never risk my neighbour's, or anyone else's, health in reality as I know to keep internal medicines separate from externals as much as possible. This is mainly because of the risk of cross bacterial contamination, but I did hear of a well-meaning husband confusing calamine lotion with kaolin mixture. He rushed to the aid of his wife, who had an upset stomach. The doses of calamine he administered orally to her did not help!

Some waterworks misunderstandings

Whenever I'm lecturing a group of nurses, I like to share stories from my career to illustrate my points. In return, the nurses often approach me at the end of the lecture to share stories of their own.

One nurse told me about visiting a lady at home following her consultation with her doctor. The nurse entered the house to find the patient confused regarding the doctor's visit, so she asked what the issue was, knowing that this particular patient had a history of urinary tract infections.

'It's this,' said the lady, showing the nurse a urine specimen bottle.

'Did the doctor ask you to provide a urine sample and take it to the surgery?'

'Yes he did, but I am not sure what to do. He said, "Please provide a mid-stream sample." But we live by a canal.'

A district nurse told me how she visited a patient who asked how she was expected to take her medicine. The nurse said that she really did not understand the problem and could the patient explain a bit further, so the patient told her that the instructions on the medication told her to 'Take in water.'

'But I don't have a bath,' she wailed, 'so how am I supposed to take them while I'm in the water? Do I have to go to the swimming pool to take my medication? Because that would just be silly.'

Silly. I couldn't have put it better myself.

Patient-resistant caps

Child-resistant packaging enclosures were first used in 1967 and soon became the norm on medication containers. Designed to make it difficult for children to access medications, unfortunately they also tend to make it difficult for the elderly and infirm.

I remember visiting an elderly lady who was having difficulties opening her medication bottles. She showed me to a seat at her kitchen table, then went at my request to fetch her medicines to show me the problems she was having.

'Here they are, dear,' she said, placing a box on the table in front of me, then shuffling into a seat opposite. As I took each bottle out one by one and examined it, I could feel my eyebrows rising. Every single container had a large hole in its brown plastic coat.

She informed me that she put her poker in the fire until it was red and plunged it into the bottle. She could then shake out the tablets.

'It's the only way I can get at them, dear,' she said. 'These new-fangled tops have the very beating of me.'

Another lady showed me her bottles of tablets, upside down and resting on the white child-proof (and, it would seem, patient-proof) caps. They were all neatly lined up on the top of the gas fire –which of course is where all good medicines are kept – and every bottle had the bottom sawn off.

'My neighbour did it for me,' she explained cheerfully. 'He picks up my prescriptions for me, and when I told him I was having no end of trouble getting these funny caps off, he said, "We can't have that" and went at them with a hacksaw. Works a treat, it does.'

An elderly gentleman with a similarly DIY-based approach had devised an ingenious way of dealing with the child-proof caps by drilling through the side of the white cap and inserting a self-tapping screw. This enabled him to use the screw to lever off the cap whenever he needed to access the medication.

The tablet bottle, meanwhile, looked like a Dalek.

But the best system I saw was a line of tablet bottles screwed by the caps to a long shelf in a gentleman's lounge. At head height, they were suspended from the shelf like a line of optics behind a bar. He could select which tablet he wanted, unscrew the bottle from the cap and remove his medication, then replace the bottle into its cap when he'd finished.

Alternatively, all these people could have simply asked for ordinary tops...

Chapter 6 – Do We Really Understand Our Bodies?

Some people, for whatever reason, have a tendency to become very confused by a visit to a clinic.

What do I mean by this? I'll show you with a few examples.

Handing over a prescription to a patient, I instructed him to apply the ointment to his skin flaps and skin folds twice daily, as he'd been advised by his dermatologist. Expecting him to take the jar of ointment and leave, confident that no one could misunderstand such simple instructions, I was a little surprised when he just stared back at me blankly.

'So, where should I put it?' he asked eventually.

'On your skin flaps and skin folds,' I repeated patiently.

'And where are they?'

'I don't know,' I replied. 'You're the one who's got them.'

Dispensing a jar of ointment to another patient, I informed him that he was to apply it to his trunk.

'How do I do that?' he said. 'I haven't got one.'

'One what?'

'A trunk,' stroking his nose.

'No, it means the trunk of your body. The large middle bit.'

'Well I've never heard it called that before.'

When I dispensed a tube of cream to yet another patient and got a quizzical look in return, I knew to expect the unexpected.

Oh no, here we go again.

Sure enough, 'It says on this label, "Apply locally", but I live ten miles away,' he said. 'Is that local enough?'

A case of over medication

One of the jobs of a hospital pharmacist when a patient is admitted is to check their prescribed medication to make sure that there are no dangerous interactions or wrong doses for the patient. This puts me in mind of an encounter with an elderly gentleman – let's call him Mr T – at the large general hospital I worked in during my early years as a qualified pharmacist. He had just been admitted and, like all patients, he had been routinely asked to bring in his medications to ensure continuity if necessary. Mr T, it seemed, had arrived with three carrier bags completely full of medications, and the ward doctor wanted me to sort out what he was actually taking.

I approached Mr T, noticing that he looked a bit vacant.

'Hello, Mr T, I am the ward pharmacist. Tell me, do you take all of these medicines?'

Mr T was meticulously unpacking his bags and lining the packs up on the bed, and I could see that there were already over twenty different kinds of medication.

'Aye, lad, I've not much time to do anything else.'

Wondering about a life that revolved around nothing more than taking medication, I sorted out the packs and bottles into related groups and began my drug review.

'Mr T, can you remember what your problem was to start with? What was the first medicine you were prescribed?'

Despite looking a little vacuous, Mr T was a bright enough man and could recall the timeline of his problems exactly. He had acquired all his medicines over a twelve-month period, and the first had been for a pain in his hip. At the age of eighty-five, he would have been doing pretty well if that was his only ailment.

But it wasn't his only ailment. Not by a long way.

The medication he had been given for his painful hip is one that's best taken with food to avoid stomach upsets, but Mr T had ignored this instruction and taken it whenever he happened to remember, which tended not to be at mealtimes. Subsequently, he had been given a second drug to reduce the acid content of his stomach and relieve the troubles brought about by his careless taking of his hip pain drugs.

Unfortunately, Mr T was susceptible to fluid retention, a rare but recognised side effect of both the drugs he was now taking.

You can guess what happened.

In time, Mr T was put on to more medication to alleviate the water retention he was suffering as a result of the medication he was already taking. The instructions on the pack said, 'Take one tablet daily', and his doctor recommended that he take them in the morning. Having already shown a healthy (or should that be unhealthy?) disinclination to follow instructions of any kind, Mr T took no notice of this suggestion and took his diuretic just before going to bed. Oh, and he was also on sleeping tablets to make sure he would have a sound night's sleep...

...And a wet bed the following morning.

Back to the doctor went Mr T, the pain in his gut having flared up again, and he was duly diagnosed as having Angina. Naturally, this led to more medication, which led to more fluid retention. Poor Mr T seemed to be going round in circles with his medication to counteract the side effects of medication, but when he started to resemble the Michelin man, his doctor had to act.

He gave Mr T more diuretics.

'I was like Niagara Falls,' said Mr T, smiling wistfully at the memory of the relief.

Unfortunately, Mr T's relief was short lived. When the body loses a large amount of fluid, it also loses the element potassium, which is essential for the smooth working of muscles. Without it, a person will feel tired all of the time, their muscles finding it difficult to function properly, and the worst-case scenario is that the heart will stop beating, and the patient wakes up dead.

All this was going on in Mr T's poor eighty-five-year-old body. He reached the point where his legs were cramping and he felt very weak, and the inevitable medication to counteract the night cramps gave him tinnitus. So, he had a pain in the hip, gut ache, fluid retention, fluid loss, muscle cramps and ringing in his ears. Could it get any worse?

Of course it could.

The medication Mr T was taking to counteract his angina was causing him to suffer from a continuous throbbing headache, and he didn't like this one bit. He returned yet again to his doctor to complain that he couldn't live with the headaches, and received Zapain (Codeine plus Paracetamol). And then he was fine?

Actually, no. The Zapain may have cleared the pain in his head, but the relief came at a cost – constipation. Next in the line of drugs laid out on Mr T's bed was a pack of laxatives. I could have sworn Mr T looked upon this packet with particular fondness.

At this point, Mr T's consultant, a well-respected care of the elderly physician, joined me and asked my opinion.

'It's quite simple,' I replied, picking up packs of medication at random and waving them in his face. 'I believe this man is being poisoned by too much medication.'

Mr T glared at me and swiped the medication packets out of my hand, gathering them to his breast. I should really have known better than to criticise his precious tablets – after all, he'd already told me once that his whole life revolved around taking them.

The consultant, however, didn't know this. 'I have been reviewing your case notes and I have to agree with my learned pharmacist colleague. You *are* being poisoned.'

At the moment he uttered the word 'poisoned' in his clear voice, the entire ward fell silent. For a couple of seconds, you could have heard a pin drop, and then pandemonium broke out. Patients started shrieking in panic, others tried to climb out of their beds and flee. The menus for the evening meal flew into the air, no one prepared to risk another mouthful of hospital food. Nurses rushed here and there, calling for backup as they tried desperately to calm the worried patients down. And in the midst of all this chaos, the consultant calmly carried on with his diagnosis.

'Mr T, we will stop all of your medications and you will feel like a new man in a week's time. You are in the right place; we can keep an eye on you.'

The consultant smiled at me and walked off the ward, oblivious to both the panic he'd caused and Mr T's open-mouthed indignation.

My heart missed a beat as I looked at Mr T. He was making a valiant attempt to stuff his medication back into his bags as a couple of nurses, who'd just succeeded in persuading the gentleman in the neighbouring bed that his broken leg would heal a lot more quickly if he lay down again and abandoned his escape plans, wrestled them away from him. I, unfortunately, was no help to them at all, lost as I was in my own jumbled thoughts.

What if I had got this wrong? Was Dr Death about to strike again?

Four days later, I walked back on to the ward and Mr T's bed was empty. Panic! Was he dead? And if he was, why was I hearing his voice booming from the far end of the ward? Had his ghost come back to haunt me for my error of judgment?

'Do you want one sugar or two?'

Well, I've never known a ghost to serve tea on a hospital ward. Glancing over timidly, I saw Mr T wheeling the tea trolley along the central aisle, as spritely and alert as I've ever seen an octogenarian look.

This time, the relief was all mine. Internal relief, that is. I'll leave the diuretics to Mr T – although, it would seem, he had left them behind too, and was looking all the better for it.

Pharmacist one, over-medication nil!

There is an epilogue to this tale. I was in the town centre a couple of weeks later and saw Mr T carrying two full carrier bags. Greeting him warmly, I wondered how on earth he'd managed to hoard so much medication again in such a short space of time, but luckily my concern was unfounded. The bags were full of food, not medicines.

'I remember you,' said Mr T, resting his bags on the pavement and fixing me with a glare. 'You're that fella from the hospital, the one that took away all my medicines.'

'That's right,' I said, my confidence wavering a little. 'You're looking very well…'

'Huh! Bloody hospital. I'll have you know, I've still got a pain in this bloody hip.'

Chapter 7 – Progress

In 1990 I was given a sizeable budget from the Regional Resource Management Project, which was being trialled in many hospitals. The budget came complete with an accountant, an office, an IT trainer and a nurse.

What could possibly go wrong?

There were some massive positives from the project. My team introduced computerised word processing to the medical secretaries and they loved it. We helped the Pathology Department introduce a completely new system to record results and a nursing management system to help nurses record their work on the ward. Instead of viewing X-rays on a light box from a negative, doctors were now able to use a desktop viewing system. And naturally the pharmacy benefitted too with a state-of-the-art computer. In terms of systems, all was good.

However, as change of any sort is wont to do, this massive leap forward in technology did cause friction in some quarters. It was now feasible to compare consultants' workloads, and being held accountable wasn't something that sat too well with some of them.

Oblivious to this friction and brimming with confidence about the positives of the new systems, I set off to give a presentation to senior medical and nursing staff, showing what information was now available for managers to use. Expecting my talk to be as well received as the systems had been elsewhere in the hospital, I was totally unprepared for the waves of palpable negativity coming from my audience.

Eventually, a consultant sprang to his feet, scowling furiously. 'Are you telling me that we have bought this system?' he snarled. 'What a waste of time and money – money that should be spent on patient care! Computers have no future in hospitals.'

Deaf to my valiant attempts to explain that the information technology would increase the time for patient care by streamlining all the administrative work that went with running a hospital, he turned on his heels and stormed out of the room.

The resource management project ran for four years and enabled the introduction of efficient departmental systems, but it's primary aim, which was to present the chief executives with a dashboard on their desk that they could interrogate to see where savings could be made, never really took off. Despite this, the project was widely acclaimed as a success, and as a result I was asked to head up a new group called the Professions Allied to Medicine, giving physiotherapy, occupational therapy, dietetics, podiatry, the spirituality department and other less well-defined groups that attached themselves to the hospital direct access to the management board, with me acting as mediator.

My first job was to dissuade a group of tree huggers from holding hands around a very old tree in the hospital grounds. The tree was under threat of being cut down because it was huge, diseased and blocking light from the wards, but inevitably, the tree huggers wanted to save it.

What a task and a half that was: on one side, the ever practical hospital authorities presented me with indisputable evidence that the tree was beyond saving and had to go. On the other side, the self-proclaimed 'environmentalists' responded to any attempt at a measured argument by upping the volume of their chanting.

'Join us, Brother,' they wailed. Clutching hands reached out, and before I could open my mouth to protest, I was drawn into their circle to pay homage to Ye Olde Tree.

I wasn't about to give up on my reason for being there that easily. 'Well, it's like this, you see…'

'Tree Spirit, Tree Spirit, hear our prayer!'

'The tree can't survive much longer…'

'Tree Spirit…'

'It's riddled with…'

'HEAR US, oh Tree Spirit…'

'…and is likely to fall at any time…'

'HEAR OUR PRAYER!'

With a great deal of difficulty, I managed to extract myself from the tree worshipping circle and return to the relative normality of the hospital building. After discussion with the chief executive, I returned to the tree huggers with trepidation and a plan to replace the old tree with two healthy young trees.

To my surprise, the tree huggers had disappeared, and the exhausted and dying tree stood alone in the grounds. I later learned that plans for a new road a couple of miles away had given the 'environmentalists' a far more alarming cause for concern than the fate of one tree, so they'd taken themselves off en masse to make trouble for the highways agencies.

All's well that ends well – for the hospital anyway. I'm not sure how well the new road fared against the tree huggers, but I'm sure they'd be pleased to know that the Tree Spirit did in fact hear their prayer and the two young trees are flourishing, bringing a great deal of wildlife into the hospital grounds.

Marathon man

To keep myself sane during this time of managerial pressure, I threw myself into a rigorous training routine with a view to running various marathons and raising money for charity. I met with a group of fellow enthusiasts (nutters), spending my Sunday mornings running 16 miles to the top of a local fell and back, but the thrill of crossing the finishing line after over 26 miles of pushing my body to the limit made it all worthwhile.

The most exciting competitive run I did at the time was the world-famous London Marathon and it was amazing. The atmosphere generated by the spectators was fantastic, and because I had my name on my vest, I had the bonus of people shouting, 'Come on, Steve,' as I ran past them. It felt like the whole world knew me!

After finishing in a highly respectable time of 4 hours, 12 minutes, I was ravenously hungry and devoured two free tuna sandwiches in quick succession. Not a good idea. I threw up at Victoria Station, much to the disgust of my fellow travellers.

Media star

My interest in the correct use of medicines led to me applying for the position of Director of Pharmacy at a large teaching hospital. Why not?

This was a major job. The previous pharmacy management team had left over a whole load of issues, and the resulting unrest had led to many staff following suit. My first aim was to stabilise the situation.

I held a staff meeting and explained that I was a local lad who had been born in that hospital. 'You cannot kid a kidder,' I told my new colleagues. I wanted honesty above all.

And I got it at the very first ward sisters' meeting I attended.

'Your pharmacy is the worst department in this hospital!'

Don't pull your punches, will you, sisters?

I have always prided myself on having the best department in the hospital, not the worst. It took six years of hard work to turn it around, but turn it around I did. My new team re-established a link with the university that had been lost, and gradually people started wanting to work for this great hospital department again. We even won an Investors in People award.

And the newfound respect we received didn't stop there. As chief pharmacist, I was sometimes asked to comment on drug-related themes for TV soaps, including the long running British stalwart *Coronation Street*. This I felt was a real honour and a great opportunity to open the eyes of the public to the realities of medication in a way they could relate to.

Do you want salt with that?

During this exciting time, I still kept up with my clinical involvement, especially on the rehabilitation and elderly wards. It was on the rehabilitation ward that I came across the patients all sitting around a long table, about to eat their lunch.

'There is no salt on this table!' one of the patients shouted at me as I stopped to pass the time of day. Well, there's nothing like getting straight to the point.

Wanting to keep the patients as contented as possible, I duly took myself off to the ward kitchen, found the salt and returned to the table with it.

'There you are,' I said, handing it to the patient with a smile.

'What are you giving me that for?' she replied.

'You asked for salt,' I said, my smile faltering.

'No I didn't. I was just letting you know there wasn't any.'

'So, does anyone else want salt with their dinner?'

A few of the other patients responded with a no; most just kept on munching their food without so much as a glance in my direction. I could only guess that they were happy with the way it tasted.

Placing the salt pot on the table, I slunk away. So much for my community spirit.

A helping hand

Several years ago, I counselled an elderly nun about the correct use of her medication.

A week later I received a small, beautifully decorated card from her, saying:

I slept and I dreamt that life was all joy;

I awoke and saw that life was but service;

I served and understood that service was joy.

Rabindranath Tagore

That says it all about the NHS.

I was always willing to help in any situation in the hospital, so when I got a call from a manager asking me to assist with moving a corpse to the mortuary, I readily agreed. The corpse, in a coffin-shaped wooden box, was huge. The deceased must have been at least 40 stone, so the large lifting truck we used in the pharmacy was certainly going to have its work cut out.

Everything started well. Several porters heaved the box on to the wheeled truck and we pulled it along the corridors. But when we tried to take the corpse outside to access the mortuary, the base of the truck refused to negotiate the metal bar at the bottom of the door.

Then the pharmacy porter came up with an ingenious plan. If we raised the base of the truck by pumping the handles, we would lift it high enough to clear the metal bar. Unfortunately, as the base lifted away from the ground, the coffin and its heavyweight occupant also rose up and hit the doorframe with some force. With a loud crunch, the whole frame collapsed around the coffin, leaving porters and pharmacists alike diving for cover. No patients were hurt, the deceased gentleman remained lying in his coffin as if nothing had happened, but I have to admit our pride took a bit of a knock.

Singing the blues

I developed a habit of going for a walk in the local town at lunchtime to get away from the day-to-day demands of the job when I was chief pharmacist of the large teaching hospital.

I was walking past a row of shops not far from Manchester United's ground, Old Trafford, one cold and wet day. Huddling into my coat to protect myself from the elements, I felt in the pockets to see if I had anything to keep my head warm. To my relief, I pulled out a cap – with Manchester City's badge on the front. Possibly not the best place in the world to reveal myself as a follower of the blues, but it would have to do. It was a grim old day.

Cap on my head, I scuttled on my way, head down, trying to remain anonymous. Some hope! I'd hardly taken a dozen steps before a jeering voice followed me on the icy breeze.

'Hey you, you've got some bird muck on your cap.'

Undeterred, I kept on strolling along. Equally undeterred, my new companion kept pace with me.

'Oi, I'm talking to you. There's only one team in Manchester. And that is?'

Hands in pockets, mouth clamped tightly shut, I put all my faith in my selective deafness and carried on walking.

'Shall I give you a clue?'

'No thank you,' I muttered under my breath.

'They don't play in flippin' blue.'

Yes they do, I thought. Better not to share that one out loud, even under my breath.

'United! United!' My unwanted follower had become followers as the red menace's taunts had caught the attention of other supporters of his team. Realising I had acquired an entourage numbering at least ten men, all intent on chanting me into submission, I disappeared into the nearest shop.

To my relief, that's all it took to shake my Manchester United following. With a smile, I recognised the irony of a group of Man U fans following City, and wished I had thought to comment on this while they were still on my tail. Or perhaps not. After all, I had been a tad outnumbered.

Looking around my new surroundings, I found to my delight that I had strayed into a well-known baker's cafe. A hot tea would be just the ticket in such inclement weather. Paying for my tea, I then headed for the exit, ready to make my way back to the hospital to return to work.

A man was standing outside the shop as I left, shivering in the cold, a cup held out in front of him. Poor devil – fancy being homeless on an awful day like this. No, I didn't fancy it, one little bit, yet that was life for this poor man.

Feeling generous, I pulled my change from my pocket and dropped it in his cup. Plop! The cup was full of coffee, and far from being homeless and down on his luck, it would seem the man was actually just waiting for his friend to pay for his lunch.

I walked away without a backward glance, as quickly as my legs would carry me, vowing to give that part of town a wide berth in future.

Chapter 8 – The Medical Police

Black Wednesday

From time to time, doctors gave us pharmacists the title of medical police, and personally I took pride in it. It certainly beat being called parasites, as one ungrateful surgeon had done.

As the medical police, we were the last line of defence between patients and doctors, protecting the former from the occasional errors of the latter. If the prescription asks for the wrong drug for the patient's ailment, or the right drug with the wrong dosage, it's the job of the medical police to notice and rectify the error.

Doctors are highly intelligent and trustworthy people, so errors are rare. But everyone can make a mistake, especially on the notorious Black Wednesday – the day when new doctors are allowed to prescribe for the first time.

It was on Black Wednesday that I received a summary for a patient who was about to be discharged from the hospital. This summary contained a list of medications that the patient had been prescribed, and a copy went to the patient's GP to ensure continuation of the treatment.

My role as medical policeman was to ensure that all the details were correct. As I checked this particular discharge prescription against the in-patient drug chart (which details all drugs taken pre and post admission), something about it leapt from the page and caught my attention.

MST 30mg BD is an abbreviation for slow release morphine twice daily, but the patient in question had been on a short-stay surgical ward where drugs of that strength would rarely be administered. I checked the patient's drug chart to see if it was a regular medication of his, but he hadn't received any morphine while in hospital. He had in fact only received a couple of doses of Codeine 15mg, a painkiller with a tenth the strength of morphine, to combat post-operative pain.

It turned out that a newly qualified doctor had thought it would be a good idea to prescribe a slow-release painkiller. However, as little as 30mg of morphine could be fatal, or at least be the beginnings of a long-term drug habit.

The curse of the hand-written prescription

Numerical and dosage errors can occur on drug charts in the hospital, grams being mixed up with milligrams, milligrams being mixed up with micrograms, and it's essential that these errors are caught before the medication is prepared. For example, a patient being prescribed 62.5mg of Digoxin, which slows the heart rate, instead of 62.5mcg would receive a dose 1,000 times higher than it should be and their heart would stop. Fortunately, errors such as these are rare, and when they do occur, they're always picked up by the medical police of nurses or pharmacists.

While misspelling and illegible prescriptions have been the cause of many an error, electronic prescribing, where doctors no longer have to write anything as the prescriptions are all on the computer screen, have not proved to be the panacea many hoped for. A patient at a general hospital had been prescribed penicillamine, a powerful drug used to counteract rheumatoid arthritis, four times daily. This was highly irregular – penicillamine is usually only given once, possibly twice daily. When I received this e-prescription, I immediately looked into why this drug had been prescribed at all, let alone in such high doses.

Apparently, the patient had had tonsillitis and the doctor had intended to prescribe *penicillin*. When he had opened the drop-down menu, a simple slip of the hand had resulted in him clicking not on the drug he wanted to prescribe, but on the similarly named but completely different medication directly above it. By the time I uncovered the error, the patient had already been taking the wrong medication for two days. Thankfully, although it had done nothing to clear up his tonsillitis, he didn't appear to have suffered any ill effects.

Of course, pharmacists aren't immune to making mistakes themselves when they're dispensing medicines. Checking a prescription, a newly qualified pharmacist had prepared for blue and pink tablets, I noticed the tablets were wrongly labelled. The 5mg tablets had 3mg on the label, the 3mg showed 5mg.

On further investigation, I discovered there was a very simple reason for this error: the pharmacist was colour blind.

I totally respect doctors, but mistakes do happen, and to my mind, one of the most important roles of the pharmacist is to ensure that doctors' prescribing is held to account. This is a reason why the Shipman case is so disappointing to me as a pharmacist. It beggars' belief that his prescribing practices went unchecked for so long. Thankfully, things are much more controlled now with tighter rules and regulations, so possibly something good did come out of this shocking and tragic case.

A sad lesson

When I began in pharmacy, questioning a doctor's prescribing habits wasn't the norm. I was working as a locum in a chemist shop back in the early days of my career, and was asked to dispense two boxes of Pethidine (the opioid-based painkiller often used in childbirth) for a doctor and his wife. Baffled, I examined their history, and saw that both were prescribed the drug on a monthly repeat prescription.

The prescription was signed by the doctor himself. Such self-prescribing of powerful controlled drugs seemed to me to be totally unethical, unsafe and inappropriate, but guidelines at the time were only seen as advisory. The fact that this doctor and his wife both had the same repeat prescription for a drug that was rarely used in the community screamed out to me that they needed help, but as I was just a locum in the area, I had little chance of being able to investigate it.

I asked colleagues in the shop whether the authorities knew about this doctor's self-prescribing, and the drug he was prescribing for himself and his wife, and they assured me that that it was being monitored. Inevitably, I was soon moved from the area and lost touch with the case, but I have often wondered what happened to the doctor and his wife.

A similar incident occurred when I was asked by a doctor to complete a prescription for himself for antidepressants. He said that his own GP had initially prescribed them, but he had run out and needed some more urgently. At the time, I took the doctor's word. It was a matter of trust – the doctor knew best.

Not long after the incident, the doctor hanged himself and committed suicide. The antidepressants had been a call for help, but at the time I was too young and inexperienced to understand.

It was a sad but important lesson that has stayed with me for my entire career.

Pharmacy dispensing robot

Electronic prescribing will become the norm in hospitals, along with robotic dispensing. While I was working at the large teaching hospital, I had the opportunity to go to Germany to see robotic devices in action in *apoteke* shops.

It was fascinating. The pharmacist took the prescription and entered the detail on to a screen. In a back room, a robotic device then picked the medication off the shelf and labelled it, while the pharmacist used the time this freed up to explain the dosage to the patient. As soon as the medication arrived in front of the pharmacist, rising up from the counter as if by magic, the patient knew all they needed to know about it and was ready to leave with their prescription in hand.

Back in the UK, some hospitals and e-pharmacies that offer a home delivery service are now using this technology.

Travelling the world

After six years of running my large department at the teaching hospital, I felt the stress was taking its toll. It was time to move on.

A friend had become successful in the world of information technology and was looking for someone to help to champion electronic prescribing in the hospital environment. All GP prescriptions were by then computer produced, but hospital electronic prescribing was in its infancy. I decided to give it a go.

This was an exciting time and I was thrilled to travel to Nassau in the Bahamas, Kuala Lumpur, Hong Kong, Bahrain, Perth, Hobart, Sydney, Melbourne and Auckland to promote the electronic prescribing concept. I also spent much time travelling around the British Isles and the Republic of Ireland.

In Hong Kong, I lectured at the first Hospital Pharmacy Conference, which went down well – especially with me since I got the opportunity to award a Manchester City shirt to a member of the audience who could name a Chinese City player. His reply, Sun Jihai, won him the coveted prize – coveted by me, anyway. A United supporter may not have been so impressed!

After the conference, at the celebratory dinner, I was awarded a glass trophy for the best lecture and for some reason was described as 'Bond from England'. I am quite tall at six foot, but I was bald and middle-aged, and I certainly didn't drive an Aston Martin DB5.

All this travel was to pay dividends in a most unexpected way when I flew to Australia with three colleagues. During our journey, the cabin crew on our flight came around with cards asking for feedback. Was the food OK? Had we been treated well? None of my travelling companions could be bothered to fill the cards in, so I did all four. It was easy because we had been treated well and we had enjoyed the food.

As an incentive to fill in the feedback form, the airline was offering a free flight to a mystery destination, the lucky winner being drawn out of a hat. The prize competition asked only if the winner would be prepared to travel anywhere. I said yes, not thinking there was any chance of me winning.

A few weeks later, I received an email from British Airways, addressed to the 'Lucky Winner'. *What a scam*, I thought, my finger hovering over delete. But at the last moment, I held back. There would be no harm in taking a look, surely?

It turned out to be genuine! I had won an all-expenses-paid weekend trip for two to Dallas, Texas. We were to fly first class both ways and stay at the Fairmont Hotel. I'm sure you can imagine how jealous the three other guys who had been with me on the trip to Australia were when I told them of my good fortune. I guess they will meticulously fill in every feedback form they get handed from now on.

Chapter 9 – Retirement

All good things come to an end, and so it was with my career as a pharmacist. I've often heard people say that their retirement is so busy, they wonder how they ever had the time to work. This has certainly been the case with me.

As a retired pharmacist, I have had the opportunity to share my experiences far and wide, travelling around and holding talks about the use of medicines. The name of my talk? *Keep On Taking The Tablets*, of course!

I actually started presenting talks when I was a practising pharmacist in the NHS and worked with the Speakers Finders agency, but it could be difficult to balance my speaking engagements with working full time. Luckily, I had a very able secretary who would organise my time for me. All I had to do was turn up at the right place at the right time, deliver my talk, and everyone was a winner.

This was great. Everything was going swimmingly until I turned up for a speaking engagement at a Labour Club in Merthyr Tydfil.

Right place – yes, that was where the talk was booked.

Right date – yes, I had arrived on the right day of the right month... of the wrong year.

I'd only gone and arrived an entire year too early.

My worst experience when delivering my talk was when I was hired to entertain 500 accountants at their annual dinner in a major hotel. The organiser's wife had heard me at a WI meeting and thought the talk was very funny. Unfortunately, the anecdotes of a pharmacist, a large crowd of accountants and copious amounts of alcohol are not a good mix. Trust me, they're not. After I'd been speaking for fifteen minutes, during which time my 'audience' had carried on drinking and chatting amongst themselves, I gave up the ghost and sat down, feeling more than a little disheartened.

I asked a good friend of mine, who just so happens to be a TV comedian, if he had ever failed to entertain an audience.

'Oh yes,' he said. 'The main thing is not to worry about it. If you have had success elsewhere with the same material, it is the audience that's wrong, not you. Just get back up there at your next gig and carry on, unless they start throwing things at you. Then either change your material or give up.'

Retirement hasn't just been about delivering talks, though. On my way home one night, I noticed a sign asking for volunteers to help give our local unmanned railway station a facelift. At the time, it was an utter mess – a dumping ground for litter and overgrown with weeds.

Six years on and the station is home to a wonderful garden. Large wooden statues of station masters stand tall and proud, the local schoolchildren having given them names such as Arthur Station, Wessy, Lofty and Rainbow Man.

The children and their teachers have also been a great help with planting bulbs and making bird boxes and insect houses. We even have a gnome garden – we call it our National Elf Service. The garden has won awards from the local council, and we are never short of donations to help brighten up the place.

You can have a look at the development of the station on YouTube – search for 'Friends of Westhoughton Station'.

An incident occurred not long ago when a young lady came down the sloping path to the platform where we were working. It was a Sunday, the usual train service running and passengers on the platforms, but we stood out as volunteers thanks to our high-vis jackets and gardening gloves. The young lady was clearly distressed, and having had a whole career in the business of helping people in distress, I went over to her without hesitation and asked if she was OK.

With tears in her eyes, she looked at our colourful display of tulips and daffodils. Then she suddenly spoke, and her words will remain with me for the rest of my life.

'I have been going through a hard time,' she said, her voice barely above a whisper. 'A *very* hard time. As a matter of fact, I had come down here to kill myself today. I was going to throw myself under a train. But after seeing all of this beautiful colour, your enthusiasm and your efforts to create such a lovely place, I have realised that there is still some goodness left in the world.'

At that, she turned and walked back up the path and away from the station, leaving me completely lost for words.

It just goes to show that there are many different ways in which we can all help people who are in need of healing, and it doesn't always involve medication.

Keep on Taking the Tablets

Glossary of Terms

Medicine – in this book, this is the science of preventing, diagnosing, alleviating or curing disease. The word is also used for any drug or remedy for use in treating or relieving the symptoms of disease. It is not merely a liquid to be swallowed in spoonfuls.

Medication – treatment with drugs or remedies.

Drug – any substance used in the treatment, prevention or diagnosis of disease.

Pharmacology – the science or study of drugs, including their characteristics, action and uses.

Truss – Padded belt used to secure hernias from protruding out of the stomach wall.

Episiotomy – A surgical cut made in the opening of the vagina during childbirth, to aid a difficult delivery and prevent rupture of tissues.

Opioid – drugs derived from opium that produce morphine-like effects. Primarily used for pain relief, they also have euphoric effects. Tolerance and dependence can develop with continued use.

Linctus – a syrupy medicinal preparation taken to relieve coughs and sore throats.

Aseptic – being in an area free from pathogenic organisms.

Polypharmacy – large number of medications

B.Sc. (Hons) – Bachelor of Science Degree with Honours.

M.Sc.– Master of Science degree.

MRPharmS – member of the Royal Pharmaceutical Society

Hydrocortisone cream – anti-inflammatory steroid cream

Codeine – painkiller

Keep on Taking the Tablets